This is a pair of Eddy's wellies.
Draw a line to match each letter on the
page to the welly with the same letter.

j

g

j

j

g

g

j

g

Trace over these letters.
Start at the dot and follow the arrow.

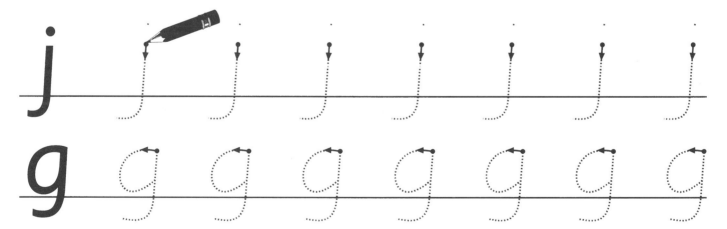

Eddy has baked some letter biscuits.

Draw over the dotted lines inside Eddy's letter biscuits.

Foundation

# Schofield & Sims

# Nursery Writing 4

**Name**

Eddy is blowing some letter bubbles.

Draw over the dotted lines inside Eddy's letters.

Trace over these letters. Start at the dot and follow the arrow.

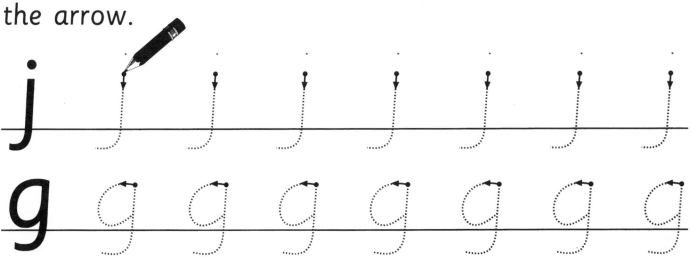

Eddy has lost some pieces from his jigsaw.
Can you help him to find them?
Draw a ring around each piece you find.

Colour the picture.

Eddy has drawn a picture of himself.

Can you copy it?

Colour your picture of Eddy.

Eddy has drawn some letters.

Draw over the lines inside Eddy's letters.

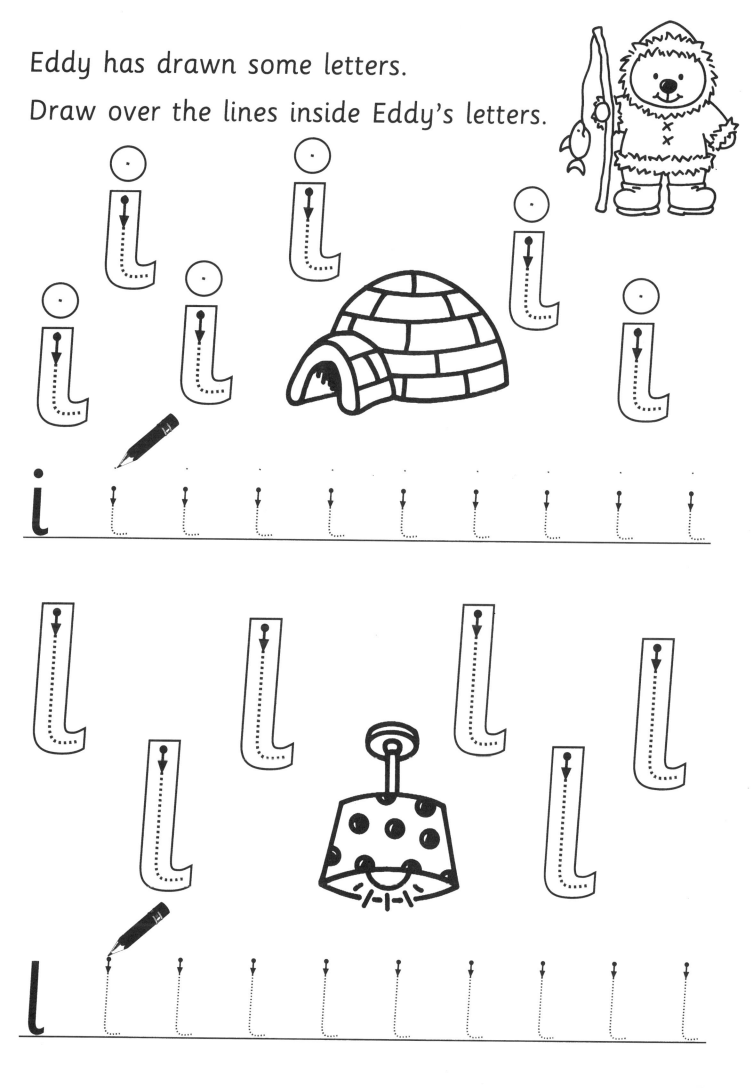

These are two of Eddy's toy planes.
Match each letter on the page
to the plane with the same letter.

l

i

i

l

i

l

i

i

l

Trace over these letters.

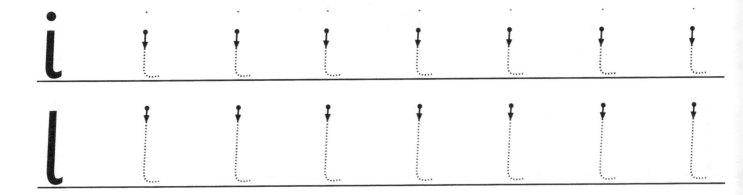

i

l

Look at the objects then look at the box.

Draw a ring around the object which comes next.

Colour the pictures.

This is Eddy's new coat.

Colour all the **u** letters pink.

Colour all the **v** letters green.

Colour all the **w** letters black.

Trace over these letters.

Start at the dot and follow the arrow.

u   u   u   u   u   u   u

v   v   v   v   v   v   v

w   w   w   w   w   w   w

Eddy has written some letters for you to trace over. Write some more of the same letter on each line.

V   v   v   v

W   w   w   w

U   u   u   u

V   v   v   v

W   w   w   w

U   u   u   u

Here are three things which begin with these letters. Trace over the dotted letters.

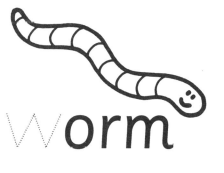
worm

van

umbrella

Colour the pictures.

Eddy has drawn some letters.

Draw over the lines inside Eddy's letters.

Colour the things beginning with **t** red.

Colour the things beginning with **f** blue.

Eddy is playing with foam letters in the bath.

Draw a line to match each letter to Eddy's letters.

Trace over these letters.

Start at the dot and follow the arrow.

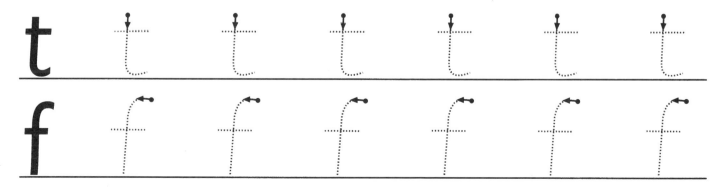

# Colour Eddy using the colour that goes with each letter.

**a** = red      **b** = yellow      **c** = black

**d** = green      **e** = pink      **f** = brown

Cross out the odd one out
on each line.

u   v   u   u   u   u

g   g   g   j   g   g

f   f   t   f   f   f

l   i   l   l   l   l

v   v   v   v   w   v

Trace over these letters.

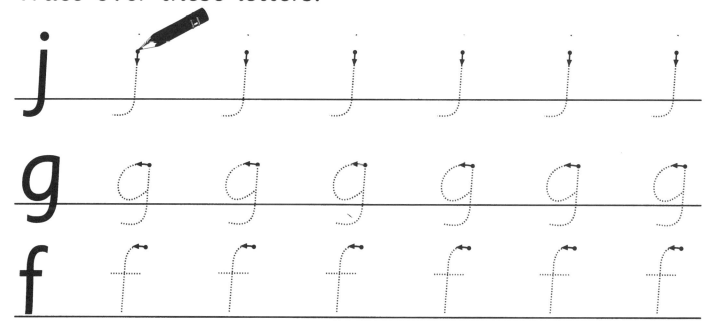

Eddy has written some letters for you to trace over. Write some more of the same letters on each line.

g   g   g   g   g

j   j   j   j   j

f   f   f   f   f

t   t   t   t   t

g   j   g   g   j

Here are some things which begin with these letters. Trace over the dotted letters.

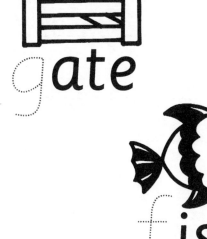

gate

fish

tree

jumper

Look at the dinosaurs.

Colour the odd one out on each line green.

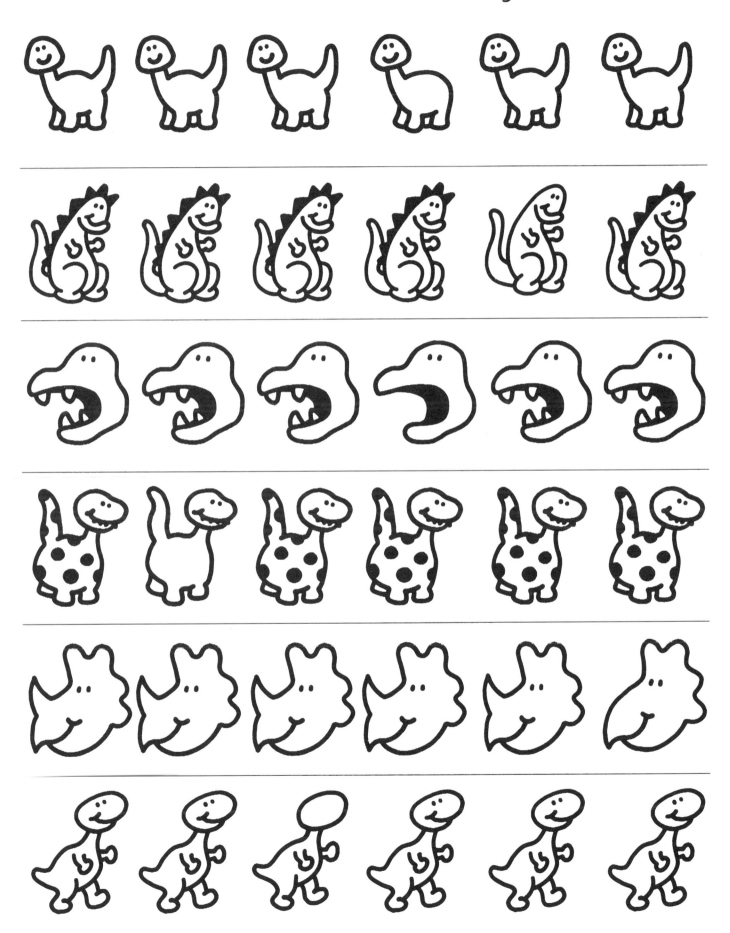

Trace over these letters.

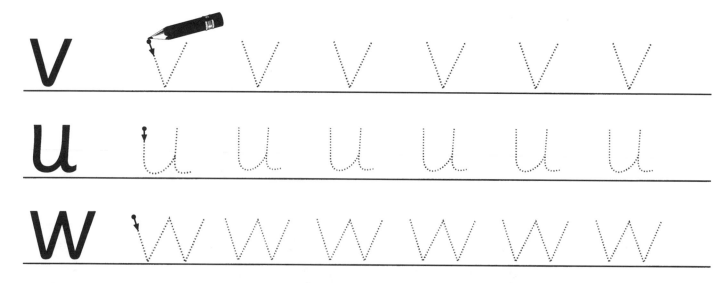

V

u

w

Colour all the things beginning with **V** orange.

Colour all the things beginning with **U** brown.

Colour all the things beginning with **W** green.

Here are some letter monsters.

Colour all the **g** monsters blue.

Colour all the **j** monsters red.

Colour all the **f** monsters yellow.

Colour all the **t** monsters purple.

Trace over these letters.

f   f   f   f   f   f   f

t   t   t   t   t   t   t

Eddy has drawn some pictures for you to colour. Trace over the dotted letters.

guitar

Lion

vase

Jam

Stamp

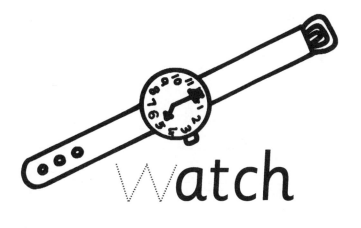

Watch

Igloo

Trace over these letters.

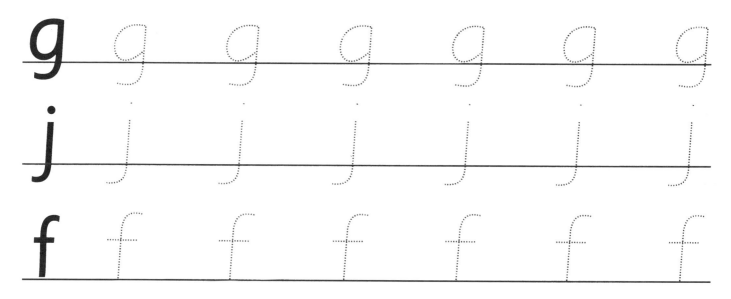

g  g  g  g  g  g  g  g

j  j  j  j  j  j  j  j

f  f  f  f  f  f  f  f

Colour all the things beginning with **g** blue.

Colour all the things beginning with **j** purple.

Colour all the things beginning with **f** yellow.

Draw a line to match each letter to the thing that begins with that letter.

b

h

d

c

m

j

Colour this picture using the colour that goes with each letter.

**g** = red    **h** = yellow    **i** = black    **j** = brown

**k** = green    **l** = purple    **m** = pink    **n** = orange

# Schofield&Sims

the long-established educational publisher specialising in maths, English and science

**Nursery Writing** is a series of graded activity books using the appealing character of **Eddy the teddy** to help young children learn letters, sounds and simple words.

**Nursery Writing Book 4** includes:

- Correct formation of the letters j/g, w/u/v, i/l and f/t
- The sounds made by the above letters at the start of a word
- Matching and tracking letters.

## The full range of titles in the series is as follows:

Have you tried **Pre-Reading Skills** by Schofield & Sims?
In this series, **Scamp the dog** helps young children to make sense of print –
by looking at picture cues and by sequencing stories, for example.

**For further information and to place your order visit
www.schofieldandsims.co.uk or telephone 01484 607080**

First edition copyright © Schofield and Sims Ltd, 1998
Twenty first impression 2016
Author: Kathryn Linaker

Printed in the UK by Wyndeham Grange Ltd, Southwick, West Sussex

MIX
Paper from
responsible sources
FSC® C010219

ISBN 978-07217-0822-5

9 780721 708225

Schofield&Sims

Dogley Mill, Fenay Bridge, Huddersfield HD8 0NQ
Phone: 01484 607080 Facsimile: 01484 606815
E-mail: sales@schofieldandsims.co.uk

ISBN 978 07217 0822 5

**£2.45
(Retail price)**

**Early Years Foundation Stage
Age range: 3–5 years**